Q IS FOR CRAZY

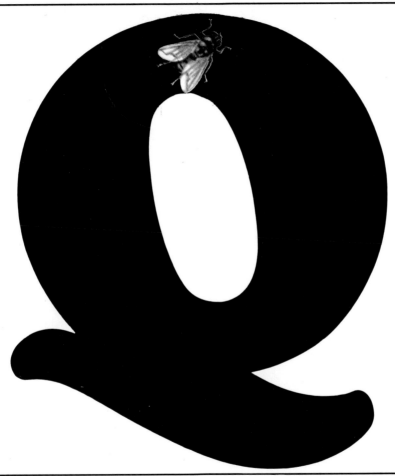

BY ED LEANDER · PICTURES BY JÖZEF SUMICHRAST

A Harlin Quist Book

Published by Harlin Quist, Inc.
Illustrations copyright © 1975
by Jözef Sumichrast
Text copyright © 1977 by Ed Leander
All rights reserved
Library of Congress Catalog Card: 77-073523
ISBN: 0-8252-7512-1
Printed in Italy by Amilcare Pizzi S.P.A.
Designed by Patrick Couratin

Think you know your ABC's ?

Then look and see what happened, please,

When one giant fly did a loop-dee-loop

And landed kerplunk ! in the alphabet soup.

In the beginning, there's Always an A −

A man, A woman, A night, A day,

A frog who sits till you want to play

And then, Annoyingly, leaps A-way.

B-ware, B wary, B where it's warm

In front of the fire... out of the storm.

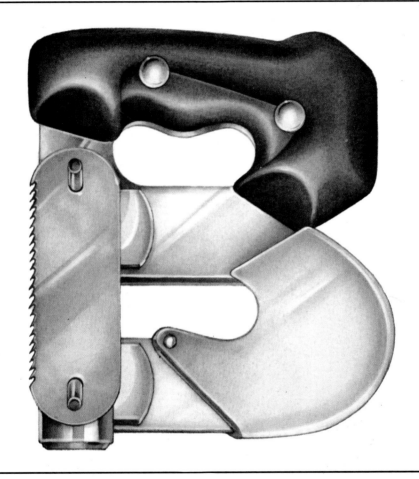

See ! It's a saw ! For cutting the wood

And keeping you feeling cozy and good.

Superwoman ! There she goes !

Watch her bend and touch her toes.

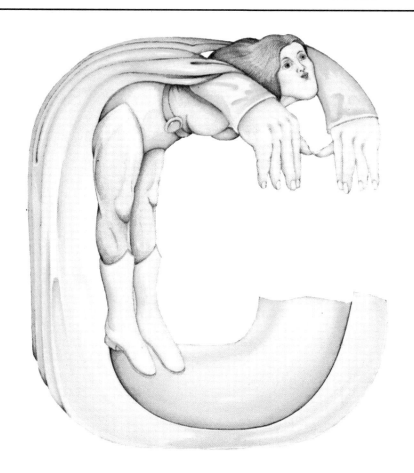

You try it too ! Let the floor be your Ceiling

And C how terrific you soon will be feeling.

D-part for adventure. Don't D-lay.

Do up your Dufflebag right away.

The ocean is Dangerous, Dark, and Deep

But it cradles and rocks you and lulls you to sleep.

"E-e-e-e !" screamed the woman who noticed a mouse.

"E-liminate him and his friends from my house !

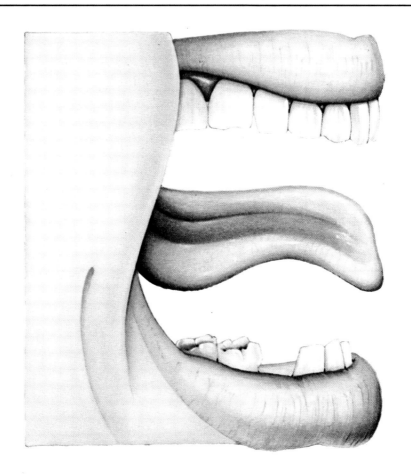

They're E-ting my cheese and it's E-dam, no less.

They're leaving me crumbs. E-gad ! What a mess !"

When hammering nails, you use all your Force

But never Forget to be careful, of course.

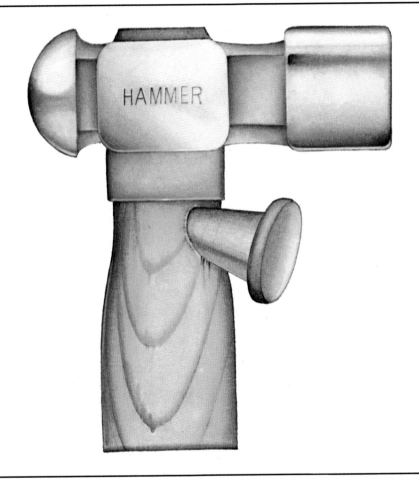

For if you're not careful, you'll do something dumb

Like missing the nail and hitting your thumb.

"Gee !" said the Gopher. "Gosh !" said the Goose.

"A Goofy Gorilla is out on the loose."

"How can you tell ?" asked the Goat in surprise.

"Who else would have blackened that poor racoon's eyes ?"

High in the sky an airplane goes by.

How does it Hang there, I wonder ?

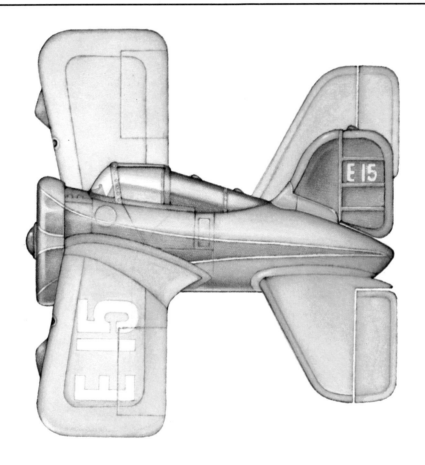

And when it Hits Heaven, How does it fly ?

Around it or over or under ?

I sure love Ice Cream and lollipops

And all the goodies they sell in shops.

I I them all, but what do I pick !

The candied apple on the wooden stick !

Jumpin' Jehoshaphat ! Look at it squirm !

A Jiggle-y, squiggle-y, wiggle-y worm !

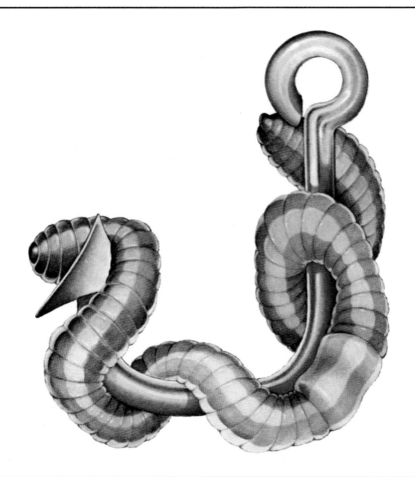

Hook him right on to a line and a pole

And fish all day long in the old swimming hole.

K makes a Klick and a Klack and a Kluck

Except in a word such as Knife.

A scissors goes Klick, but you won't find a K

If you look for the rest of your life !

L is for Laughter and Looking real Loony

And Lying around upside down.

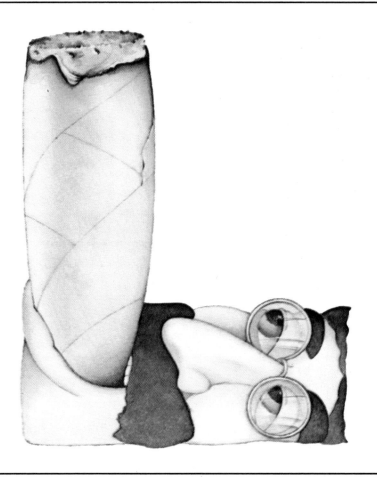

It's L-oquent, L-egant, and L-emental –

It's anything L-se but a frown.

"Hey, Mr. Mallard Duck, where are you going?"

"Down to Miami, before it starts snowing.

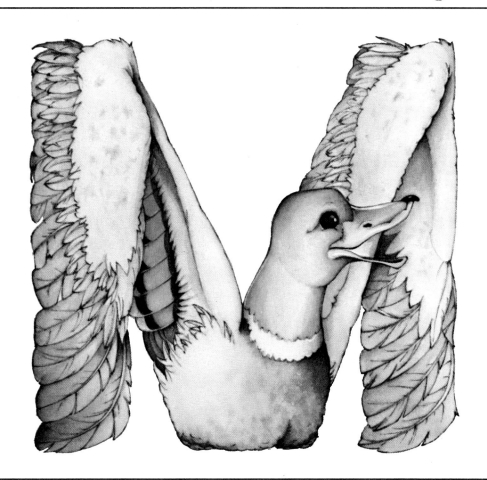

Might go to Mexico till winter ends

To Mingle, Make Merry, and Mix with My friends."

N-ytime N-yone builds something tall

N-y New building that isn't too small

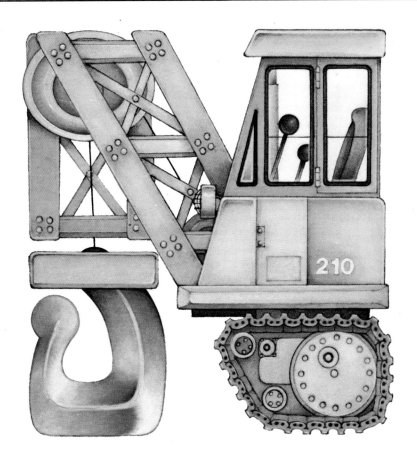

Notice the work going on at the scene...

N-ywhere Near it, you'll find this machine.

Oh! What I'd give to be in the saddle

Out in the glorious West

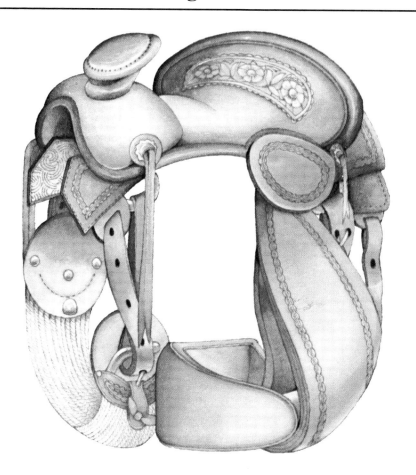

Out-riding the good guys, Out-shooting them, too...

I'd be the Out-rageously best.

Peep at Penelope, Peaceful and Pretty

Dressed all in Pink for her stroll through the city.

Proud as can be are her Dad and her Mum

While she lies there Peacefully sucking her thumb.

Q is a letter that's really Quite Queer.

It only allows a U to get near.

Wherever Q goes, there's a U right behind it –

Yes, Q is for crazy, so just never mind it!

Rajahs and Ranis who rule in the East

Go Riding and Romping on this giant beast.

R-en't they lucky ? Whatever they pack

Goes Right in the trunk and they're Right in back.

S is for Serpents who Swim in the ocean

And Splatter and Splash with their Slightery motion.

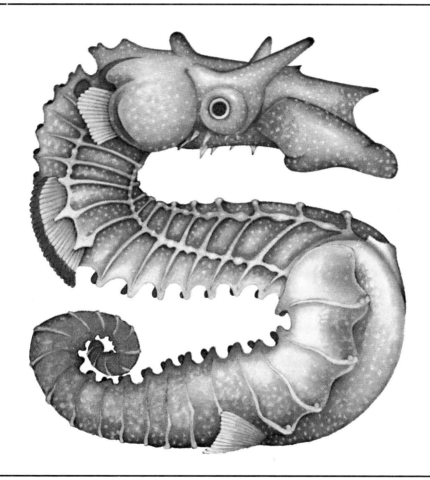

S is for Sea horses, Sailing and Sliding –

But better watch out! They're not meant for riding.

T is for Twisting and Tugging and Turning

And Trying to open the wine.

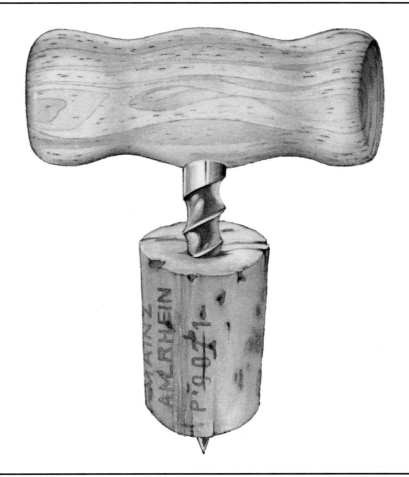

"T-rific," cries Pop as the bottle goes plop :

"Now we can sit down and dine."

U see these pants ? They're Upside down –

Unfortunately, frozen.

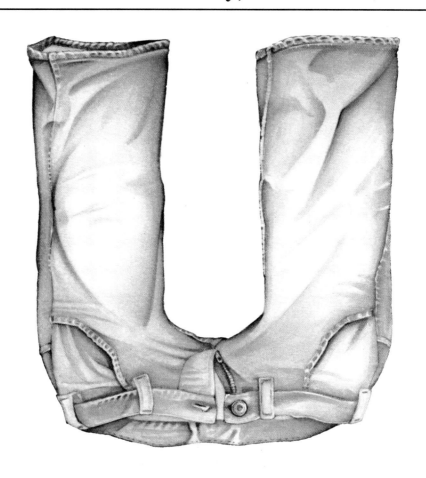

Poor Uncle has to go to town

And cannot get his toes in !

Very Valuable is the knife

It's Versatile and handy.

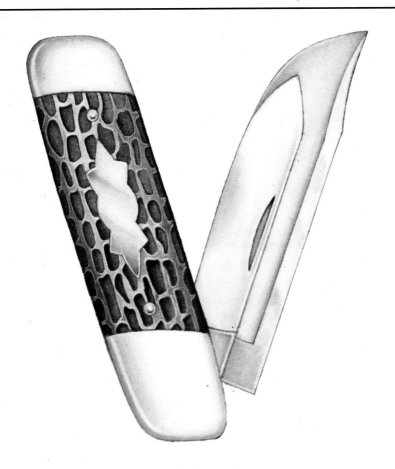

It fits in your pocket and helps you slice

Your apples and your candy.

Wow! What a muscle-man! He lifts Weights

And Weights begins With a W.

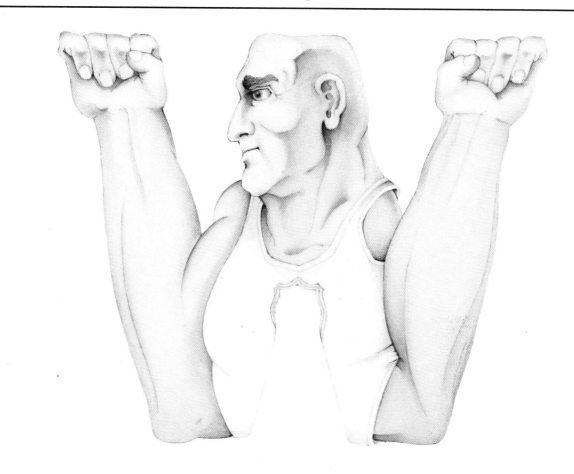

Whistle for him – he'll help you out

If anyone should trouble you.

X-amine the turtle. You'll see he's X-tended.

X-cept for his nose, he's X-tremely upended.

X-perience shows that this pose is X-ótic

X-entric, X-hausting, and X-tra neurotic.

Y in the world did somebody stop

Eating this chocolate-y pop?

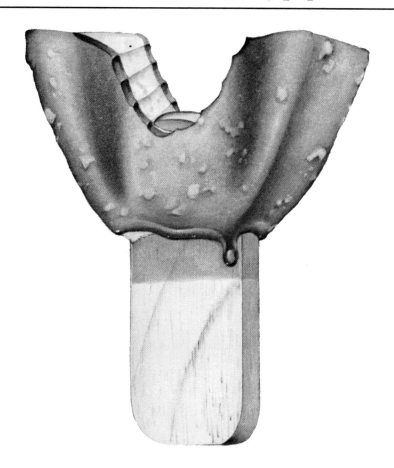

Y can't it pop right out of this book?

Then we could eat, not just look.

Zigging and Zagging and Zipping along

Policemen stop people from doing what's wrong.

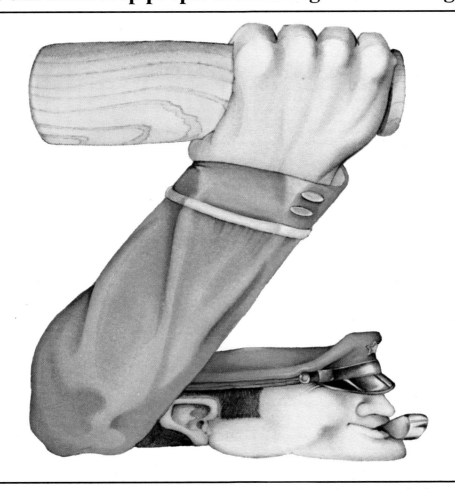

Zillions of times while we're sleeping at night

They're Zealously seeing that things are all right.

Well, now you know – from A to Z –

What fun the letters R to C.

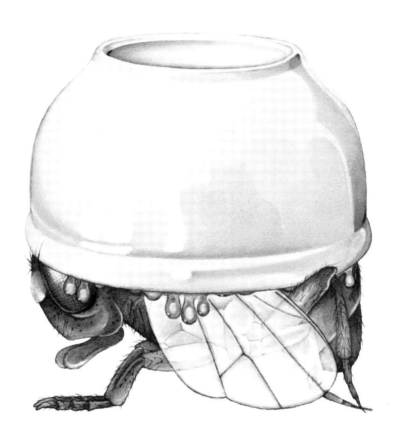

B Ys and learn all 26

And watch them change and do their tricks.